HEADLINE ISSUES

Stopping Pollution

Catherine Chambers

Heinemann
LIBRARY

www.heinemannlibrary.co.uk
Visit our website to find out more information about **Heinemann Library** books.

To order:
 Phone 44 (0) 1865 888066
 Send a fax to 44 (0) 1865 314091
Visit the Heinemann Bookshop at www.heinemannlibrary.co.uk to browse our catalogue and order online.

Heinemann Library is an imprint of Capstone Global Library Limited, a company incorporated in England and Wales having its registered office at 7 Pilgrim Street, London, EC4V 6LB - Registered company number: 6695582

"Heinemann" is a registered trademark of Pearson Education Limited, under licence to Capstone Global Library Limited

Text © Capstone Global Library Limited 2009
First published in hardback in 2009
The moral rights of the proprietor have been asserted.

Edited by Sarah Eason and Leon Gray
Designed by Calcium and Geoff Ward
Original illustrations © Capstone Global Library Limited 2009
Illustrated by Geoff Ward
Picture research by Maria Joannou
Originated by Heinemann Library
Printed and bound in China by CTPS

ISBN 978 0 431162 69 0 (hardback)
13 12 11 10 09
10 9 8 7 6 5 4 3 2 1

British Library Cataloguing in Publication Data
Chambers, Catherine, 1954-
   Stopping pollution. - (Headline issues)
   1. Pollution prevention - Juvenile literature
   I. Title
   363.7'37
A full catalogue record for this book is available from the British Library.

Acknowledgements
We would like to thank the following for permission to reproduce photographs:
Alamy Images: Leslie Garland Picture Library 21t; Corbis: Kai Foersterling/EPA 15, Reuters 6b, Peter Turnley 28; Fotolia: Bilderbox 23, Ch'lu 21, Wild Geese 25; FLPA: Chris Newbert/Minden Pictures 26; Getty: Aurora 9, Louis Psihoyos 23; Istockphoto: Phil Cardamone 9, Chris Crafter 21b, Andrew Howe 18, Manfredxy 30–31, Roman Milert 22, Jeroen Peys 16–17; NASA/GSFC/C. Mayhew & R. Simmon, NOAA/NGDC, DMSP 24b; NHPA: A.N.T. Photo Library 14b; Photolibrary: Hervé de Gueltzl/Photononstop 17b; Rex Features: Sipa Press 13b; Science Photo Library: Tony Craddock 17t, James King-Holmes 19; Shutterstock: 8, 14, Albo 32, Victoria Alexandrova 8, Elena Aliaga 10–11, Galyna Andrushko 6–7, Rob Bouwman 1, 12, David Brimm 16–17, Buquet 18–19, Alberto Calheiros 24–25, Ciapix 4b, Elena Elisseeva 26–27, Petr Jilek 19, Sergey Kamshylin 14–15, Philip Lange 7, Adam Majchrzak 5b, Mashe 28–29, Pelham James Mitchinson 10, Oculo 29, Opla 12b, Petr Nad 10–11, Thomas Nord 7c, PeJo 4–5, Andrey Pils 3, Vlade Shestakov 11, Stephen Strathdee 26–27, David Thyberg 13, H Tuller 4–5, Marc van Vuren 20, Ashley Whitworth 16, Michael Zysman 22–23; Transurban Limited: 27.

Cover photograph reproduced with permission of Istockphoto/Phil Cardamone.

Every effort has been made to contact copyright holders of material reproduced in this book. Any omissions will be rectified in subsequent printings if notice is given to the publishers.

Contents

Some words are printed in bold, **like this**. You can find out what they mean by looking in the glossary, on page 30.

The global pollution panic

AROUND 6.6 BILLION people live on planet Earth. All these people use huge amounts of food and water. They live in houses, buy goods, and travel in cars, buses, and aeroplanes. Human activities create **pollutants** and waste, which end up in the Earth's sea, soil, and sky.

Our planet is at crisis point. Pollution is affecting everything, from our health to the world around us. It is contributing to **climate change**. The good news is that we can all help to stop pollution.

The way ahead

Pollution challenges scientists to develop clean energy and products that are kinder to the environment. They are finding ways to stop pollutants from damaging our planet. Governments are banning **toxic** chemicals and waste. People are reducing what they buy and reusing what they have to stop creating so much waste.

The trees in Central Park, New York, help to keep the air clean by absorbing a lot of the carbon gases in it.

4

BEHIND THE HEADLINES

Top ten polluted cities in the world

All the cities listed below are suffering from air, soil, or water pollution. Some face problems from all three forms of pollution. Typical pollutants include **carbon dioxide** or **lead**. The top ten list of polluted cities changes every year. In 2008, they were:

Linfen, China
Tianying, China
Sukinda, India
Vapi, India
La Oroya, Peru
Dzerzhinsk, Russia
Norilsk, Russia
Chernobyl, Ukraine
Sumgayit, Azerbaijan
Kabwe, Zambia.

Up to 70 per cent of the lead used by industry goes towards making batteries. Lead pollutes the soil and water.

Travel costs the Earth

By the year 2020, there will be more than one billion motor vehicles on the world's roads. Motor vehicles release huge volumes of **carbon dioxide** gas. This gas builds up in the **atmosphere** and traps heat around the Earth. Carbon dioxide is one of the **greenhouse gases** that causes **climate change**.

Pollution on the ground

Exhaust fumes cause pollution at ground level, too. The fumes are thought to be responsible for about 24,000 deaths in Britain each year. Rain washes oil, **carbon compounds**, and tyre fragments from roads and pollutes the soil and water.

Air travel

High in the atmosphere, the gas trails of aircraft are affecting **jet streams**. Jet streams are powerful thrusts of air that help to control Earth's climate. Jet streams are changing and causing violent **cyclone** storms and **tornadoes**.

New fuels

An answer to the problems of traffic pollution could be **biofuels**. Biofuels are made from crops such as palm oil seeds. They do not give off large amounts of carbon when they burn. Most biofuels are grown by poor farmers in the developing world. However, they need to grow crops for food, not fuel.

People living in Lagos in Nigeria can only use their cars in the city every other day. This has cut down on car use in the city.

People should use public transport, not cars: Who is right and who is wrong?

FOR

Public transport is definitely better for the environment. Coaches transport many more passengers than cars and produce much less pollution per passenger. Rail travel is even more efficient in terms of the amount of fuel used and the amount of pollution produced.

Japan has one of the cleanest train services in the world.

AGAINST

Car owners argue that their vehicles are much more comfortable and convenient than public transport. People spend a lot of time waiting for buses and trains to arrive, there are often lengthy delays, the services are limited, and the tickets are simply too expensive.

Choking chimney challenge

EVERY YEAR, FACTORIES around the world release billions of tonnes of harmful gases such as **carbon dioxide** and **methane**. Inside homes, solid fuel fires such as coal, dung, and wood give off fumes many times above the safety level.

Rising temperature

In the last 150 years, the world's temperature has increased by $0.7°C$ ($1.3°F$). The rising temperatures have melted the ice caps and raised sea levels. During this time, **industrial** pollution has become a big problem. In some parts of the world, pollution is creating violent storms. In others, dry places are getting much drier.

Factory fumes

Heat from factory fumes raises the temperature of city rivers and lakes. This reduces the amount of oxygen in the water, so plants, insects, and fish cannot survive.

Factories in China are pumping out huge amounts of waste gases. Scientists do not know what effect they are having on the Earth's climate.

These lifeless watery **habitats** are known as "dead zones".

Fighting the fumes

People have realized that pollution is a big problem. Many of the world's most **toxic** gases are now banned. Some factories **recycle** heat and fumes to make energy. Others are cleaning the fumes before they are released into the air. Many factories are aiming for zero **emissions**.

FACT!

✦ According to the Environmental Protection Agency, gases from factories contribute to more than 2,800 cases of lung cancer each year in the United States.

✦ Factory fumes also contribute to 38,000 heart attacks each year in the United States.

ON THE SPOT
China

China's heavy air pollution is not often washed away by rain. Heavy air pollution stops raindrops from forming. To tackle this problem, Chinese authorities are sending aeroplanes into the clouds to "seed" or spray them with dry ice (frozen carbon dioxide) or a chemical called silver iodide. Seeding clouds makes raindrops form and clears the polluted city air.

Cloud-seeding is also used to water crops in dry places.

Nuclear power – now or never?

NUCLEAR POWER COULD be the solution to **global warming**. **Nuclear power** does not produce harmful gases. France uses nuclear power and has the cleanest air of any developed nation. It also has the cheapest electricity.

Nuclear problems

There is a big problem with nuclear power. It uses a dangerous metal called **uranium**. Uranium produces invisible, but harmful, **radioactive** waves. Nuclear waste also produces these waves. If people breathe in the radiation or swallow radioactive waste it can damage cells inside the body. It can poison land and water for many years.

Nuclear waste worries

A nuclear **reactor** produces up to 30 tonnes (29.5 tons) of radioactive waste every year. It is difficult and costly to deal with nuclear waste.

Most electricity in France is produced by nuclear energy. This produces about 1 million cubic metres (35.3 million cubic feet) of spent nuclear fuel on French soil. Most of France's nuclear waste is transported to the port of La Hague, where it is "conditioned". This means it is reprocessed and stored in thick glass. A lot of this waste can be reused as energy.

Fire alarms need to be disposed of with care because they contain a radioactive substance.

◆ Nuclear power provides 17 per cent of the world's electricity.
◆ There are 435 working nuclear power stations in the world.
◆ There are nuclear power stations in 30 per cent of the world's countries.

ON THE SPOT

Chernobyl, Ukraine

Chernobyl

On 26 April 1986, an explosion rocked one of the nuclear reactors at a site in Chernobyl in Ukraine. A huge fire destroyed most of the power station. Winds sent the radioactive smoke across Europe and as far as the east coast of America. In Chernobyl, radiation killed some people instantly. More than 350,000 people had to be resettled.

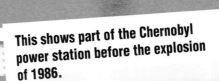

This shows part of the Chernobyl power station before the explosion of 1986.

Oil spills far into the future

Oil is a **fossil fuel** that produces harmful fumes when it burns. Oil spills kill wildlife and poison soils and waterways.

Oil spreads everywhere

Around 60 per cent of oil spills are caused by **road runoff**. This occurs when oil leaks from vehicles onto roads and into soil and water.

The oil industry accounts for 30 per cent of oil spills. These slicks coat coastlines with oil and harm wildlife, especially birds and fish. The remaining 10 per cent of oil seeps naturally from the ground and from the droplets that form in the air when oil burns.

Saving the seas

If a spill does happen, **satellite** images track it so that people on the coast can prepare. Scare cans and floating dummies are used to scare birds away from an oil spill.

Mopping up the spill

The spill itself can be contained using a **boom**. This is often made of a circle of floating logs with thick plastic skirts. The oil is cleaned using chemical foams. Sawdust and wool can also be used to mop up the oil. **Bacteria** break down the remaining droplets, but it takes time to clean up all the oil.

Most oil tankers now have thick double hulls (casing around the lower part of a ship) to stop oil from leaking.

ON THE SPOT
Alaska

Prince William Sound

In 1989, the oil tanker *Exxon Valdez* broke up off the coast of Alaska, USA. Oil from 270,000 barrels polluted 2,000 kilometres (1,240 miles) of coastline. More than 300,000 birds were killed and their nesting sites destroyed. Billions of fish eggs were destroyed. Local people say that the spill is still harming the fishing industry. The area is only just beginning to recover more than 20 years after the spill took place.

The *Exxon Valdez* oil spill was one of the worst environmental disasters in history.

Fury over forest fires

CLIMATE CHANGE HAS made the world's forests, grasslands, and scrublands very dry. They easily catch fire. Forest fires produce massive clouds of carbon gases. These pollute the air and add to the problems of climate change. On the ground, people's lives are ruined. Wildlife is killed and **habitats** are also destroyed.

Fires lit for gain

Natural fires happen every year. Many fires are caused by carelessness, such as when people drop a burning cigarette or match.

Huge areas are also burned on purpose. The fires clear the land to make way for food crops and **biofuels**. Land is burned to build houses, too.

Fire detection

A tall plume of smoke is one sign that a fire could break out. Forest rangers and fire fighters then use **satellites** to track the fires. They help to tell how the winds will spread the fires. However, satellites miss crawling wild fires in low, thick vegetation. Sensors low on the ground are used to track these.

One plant that benefits from a forest fire is eucalyptus. It grows quickly after a fire.

Fighting the flames

Forest rangers and fire fighters stop fires from spreading by chopping down trees and creating breaks throughout the forest. These are wide strips of bare or charred earth with nothing to fuel the fire. Fire-fighters tackle fires with portable water pumps. If they fail, it's time to call in the air crew.

A plane releases chemicals and water sprays to stop a forest fire raging out of control.

The number of hectares of land damaged in some recent forest fires:

✦ 2007	California (USA):	200,000 hectares	✦ 2003	Russia:	23,700,000 hectares
✦ 2007	Greece:	200,000 hectares	✦ 2003	Portugal:	350,000 hectares
✦ 2003	Australia:	60,000,000 hectares	✦ 1997	Indonesia:	10,000,000 hectares

FACT!

Paying the price of plastics

PLASTIC COSTS THE Earth. It is made from oil. When plastics are made, **toxins** are released into the air. Plastic waste kills wildlife and contaminates water.

Plastic litter spoils natural habitats.

Slow break-down

A plastic bottle takes about 450 years to break down in the sea. Fishing lines take 600 years to break down. Many fish also die because of "ghost fishing". This occurs when fish are strangled by thrown-away fishing lines. In the sea, plastics break down into almost invisible pieces. These attach to tiny **plankton**, which are eaten by fish and sea mammals. On land, many birds have plastic inside them.

Stop plastic pollution!

Reduce, reuse, and **recycle** to stop plastic pollution. Plastic bags can be used time and again. You can also use other types of bag, such as hessian. Many plastics can also be recycled to make other things, such as flooring and furniture.

Plastic bags are now banned totally in Bangladesh. Flooding is a big problem in Bangladesh. In the past, plastic bags clogged drains, making flooding worse. China banned free plastic bags from 2008.

BEHIND THE HEADLINES
Plastics transformed

There are 50 main types of plastic, and they can all be recycled. They are sorted, then made into small pellets in machines. The best plastic for recycling is called high-density polyethylene (HDPE). HDPE can be recycled into many goods, such as bottles, furniture, rubbish bins, and even your school ruler.

Designers are making items such as brooms and fashionable jewellery using recycled plastics.

Farming's chemical chaos

FARMERS ARE STRUGGLING to feed the world's 6.6 billion people. Most have to use the same land over and over again. This uses up all the **nutrients** in the soil, so farmers add **fertilizers** to the soil. Crops are also sprayed with **pesticides** to kill pests such as insects. All these chemicals are poisoning the Earth.

Water and air

Rainstorms wash chemicals into the soil. The chemicals end up in wells and run off into rivers. Research in India has shown that this runoff is worse where thick, sticky clay soils hold a lot of the chemicals. Farm animals also contribute to pollution. Cattle release millions of tonnes of **methane** into the air when they break wind. Methane gas causes more harm to the environment than **carbon dioxide**.

Stop chemical farming

Many farmers are now growing organic food. This means using animal manure (droppings) or plant material to fertilize the soil.

Pesticides kill insects that this rare yellowhammer needs for food.

Other farmers still use chemicals, but they are helping to reduce pesticide pollution by spraying their crops with smaller nozzles. This means that less pesticide is used. Dangerous spraying practices, such as wearing no protective clothing or masks, are banned in most countries.

GM crops are good for people: Who is right and who is wrong?

FOR

Scientists design genetically modified (GM) crops to resist disease and drought. This means that farmers do not need to spray the crops with chemicals, which is better for the environment. GM crops that need less water will survive better in hot countries. GM crops produce more food, too, so this means more hungry people can be fed.

GM crops are often grown in secret because some people would destroy them.

AGAINST

Many people are worried about GM crops. They do not think enough tests have been done to see if the crops are safe. They believe that GM crops will mix with other crops, especially those of organic farmers. There is also a chance that plants such as weeds will pick up the genes, making them resistant to weedkillers.

Serious sewage situation

SEWAGE POLLUTION AFFECTS some of the world's poorest people. Open drains in towns and cities expose millions of people to disease and pests. During a flood, the **sewage** rises with the water. Deadly diseases such as **cholera** become a problem.

Too much sewage

In the developed world, sewage systems are at breaking point. In Britain, people produce more than 75 million litres (16.5 million gallons) of sewage every day. Many sewage systems are clogged with washing detergents and fats from fast foods.

In the United States, 9,464 trillion litres (2,081 trillion gallons) of piped sewage are treated every day. The sewage flows to 20,000 treatment plants, but the system leaks. In 2002, 87 per cent of all closed beaches were due to sewage **bacteria** in the water.

Sewage systems go natural

Many modern building projects include **composting** toilets that do not need to be connected to overloaded sewage systems. Composting toilets are set over a large box or pit. **Organisms** such as worms break down the sewage that drops in the pit. After a while, the sewage reaches 40–50°C (104–122°F), which kills harmful bacteria. This system uses less water, too.

Waste water without chemicals

Waste water from washing clothes is called "grey water". It can flow through pipes into a natural sewage pit. Grey water must not contain too many chemical detergents. These destroy the organisms in the pit. Borax is one safe, natural washing crystal that can be used safely in natural sewage pits.

BEHIND THE HEADLINES
Natural sewage treatment

In many countries, people are planting reed beds near ponds and lakes. The reeds are being used to treat sewage and clean waste water. The long leaves of the reeds take in oxygen from the air. The oxygen passes down to the roots and out into the water. The oxygen helps bacteria to break down sewage. Reed beds have to be fenced off so that rabbits and other animals do not nibble at the roots.

Pumps make sure the sewage reaches large reed beds.

Old sewage pipes overflow and collapse during a city flood.

21

The looming litter mountain

Some of the world's waste is dumped on the surface. It forms huge litter mountains in which pests and diseases live. The rest is buried in landfill sites. Gases build up as the waste breaks down. These gases contribute to **climate change**. A lot of waste contains **toxins** that wash into the soil and waterways.

Naples in waste

Litter is a big problem in Naples in southern Italy. All of the region's landfill sites are full. The tourist industry has lost a lot of money.

People do not like to see rubbish on the streets of the city. In 2008, the German port of Bremerhaven agreed to take away 30,000 tonnes (29,520 tons) of the rubbish.

Getting rid of rubbish

Many products are now marked with a symbol to show if they can be **recycled**. People can now buy many different products that last longer and cause less pollution, such as rechargeable batteries.

Aluminium drinks cans can be recycled, but 80 million cans are still thrown away every year.

ON THE SPOT

Cairo, Egypt

The Zabaleen are a Christian community living in the Moqattam district of Cairo, Egypt. They recycle some of the city's waste, which is brought to their streets in lorry loads. The authorities plan to pay companies to take away the waste. The Zabaleen will lose out. They want to keep recycling.

The Zabaleen separate useful materials from Cairo's waste.

✦ **Methane** forms when buried waste rots.
✦ Carbon gases and sulphur dioxide are given off when waste burns.
✦ Acids from batteries poison soils and water.

FACT!

Light darkens the shadows

LIGHT POLLUTION IS a big problem. Lights blaze from city streets, factories, and office blocks. The lights in cities create a permanent glow in the night sky. The problem is worse where tiny pieces of pollution scatter the light.

Light's not alright

Light disturbs our sleep. It stops **nocturnal** creatures from feeding and mating. Moths cannot find night-blooming plants on which to feed. Zooplankton are tiny animals that live in ponds and lakes. They are not growing properly because of light pollution. Zooplankton eat the green algae that otherwise clog up rivers and lakes.

Too bright to be safe

Too much light in cities does not prevent crime. Bright light stops the eyes adjusting to the dark. People cannot see beyond the bright light. It also darkens the shadows in which criminals can hide.

Soft but safe

New lighting gives the streets enough light to be safe. Many offices use low-level security lighting, which is cheaper and does not waste energy. New light fittings with hoods direct light beams down. Flat-lens bulbs deliver light with a narrow beam.

The bright lights of the world's cities dazzle from space.

ON THE SPOT

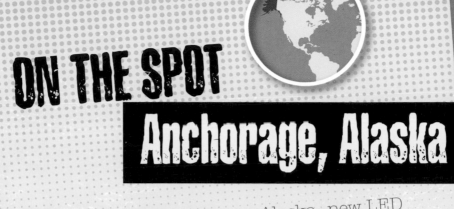

Anchorage, Alaska

In the city of Anchorage in Alaska, new LED (light-emitting diode) street light-bulbs will soon let out a brighter, whiter light. The bulbs will be protected by a curved hooded fixture. This will stop the bright light from polluting Alaska's broad, inky black skies.

The Sun sets over the city of Anchorage in Alaska. New bright LED street lamps will soon light up the city.

Noise hits the headlines

NOISE POLLUTION IS another major problem. In 2007, a report in Britain blamed noise pollution for illnesses such as depression, high blood pressure, and stress in adults. Noise pollution contributes to poor concentration and low reading levels in children. Noise and vibration from aircraft and heavy vehicles disturb wildlife. Their calls are drowned out by noise pollution.

No more noise

Stopping noise pollution means better planning. New airports are built away from **residential** areas. Flight paths are redirected away from these areas. Flights at night are reduced so people can sleep. On the roads, new surfaces are made from materials that absorb noise better. Some countries are mixing in **recycled** plastics. Thick walls act as sound buffers along ring roads in big cities.

Sonar death

Whales and dolphins are dying because noise pollution is interfering with their navigation.

Many whales end up beached on the shore because noise pollution interferes with their navigation.

These creatures find their way around by using high-pitched sound waves called **sonar**. Sonar from submarines and fishing boats are drowning out the whales and dolphins. They end up stranded on beaches and die.

BEHIND THE HEADLINES

Sound Tube sculpture

A noisy, raised highway connects many parts of Melbourne in Australia. In Flemington District, high-rise apartments are 150 metres (490 feet) away from the highway. A long "Sound Tube" now covers the road. It is a steel-framed dome with glass panels. The design captures the noise from the highway. A light display makes it glow at night.

Cars head through the "Sound Tube" on the Tullamarine Freeway in Melbourne.

Get involved!

POLLUTION AFFECTS THE quality of life for everything on the planet. It is a huge threat to life itself. There are many charities and organizations led by people who are passionate about stopping pollution and making the world a better place in which to live.

Greenpeace, Earthkind, Friends of the Earth, the Soil Association, Slow Food Movement, and the Campaign for Dark Skies are just a few examples of organizations that can help you find new ways to reduce the problems of pollution on our planet.

The polluted Yangtze River is a major health problem in China. It may be responsible for many thousands of deaths each year.

THINGS TO DO

Reduce

- Wear sweaters at home in the winter. Then you can turn down the heating.

- Pick up litter, and do not drop chewing gum. Water jets use up a lot of energy to remove gum from pavements.

- Walk or cycle to school if you can. Ask your parents to organize a car-share scheme.

- Turn off the tap when you clean your teeth. Shower instead of taking a bath. A bath uses three times as much water as a shower.

- Grow your own vegetables. They will be free from harmful chemicals, and you will not have to travel to get them. This means you will save precious energy.

Reuse

- Reuse old clothes. You could add a new belt or buttons to make them more stylish.

Growing your own vegetables will help to save energy and they taste great, too.

If you don't reuse them yourself, take them to a charity shop so other people can wear them.

Recycle

- Recycle plastic bottles, glass bottles and jars, drinks cans, newspapers, and cardboard.

- Look out for new ideas on helping our planet on www.coolkidsforacoolclimate.com

Glossary

atmosphere layer of air that surrounds the Earth

bacterium tiny living cell. Some bacteria are useful, but others cause harmful diseases.

biofuel fuel made from plants such as palm oil seeds and sugar cane

boom floating barrier

carbon compound substance that contains carbon

carbon dioxide gas released from burning fossil fuels

cholera disease caused by bacteria found in dirty water

climate change changes in the world's weather patterns caused by human activities such as burning fossil fuels

composting breaking down waste using bacteria, worms, and other creatures in the soil

cyclone rotating storm with fierce winds and heavy rain

emission substance let out from exhausts or chimneys

fertilizer substance put in the soil to help plants grow

fossil fuel fuel made from animals and plants that lived millions of years ago

global warming increase in the average temperature at Earth's surface

greenhouse gas gas that traps heat from the Sun

habitat place where animals and plants normally live in the wild

industrial to do with industry

jet stream powerful wind that circulates high in Earth's atmosphere

lead heavy metal that can slowly poison the body

methane greenhouse gas produced by animals and rotting material

nocturnal active at night

nuclear power electricity generated from a nuclear reaction

nutrient substances in our food that are needed for good health

organism living thing – some organisms are very small

pesticide substance sprayed over crops to kill pests such as insects

plankton tiny sea creature

pollutant chemical that causes pollution, such as certain carbon compounds and metals such as lead

radioactive having atoms that break up and send out harmful rays as radiation

reactor vessel in which a chemical or nuclear reaction takes place

recycle to use something again instead of just throwing it away

residential containing people's homes, not offices and factories

road runoff oil that leaks from motor vehicles onto roads and into soil and waterways

satellite space vehicle placed in orbit around the Earth and used for communication or to gather data

sewage all the liquid and solid waste material from toilets and sinks, which is carried away by drains and sewers

sonar high-pitched sound waves used to navigate and locate objects

tornado violent storm or whirlwind

toxic poisonous

toxin chemical that is poisonous

uranium rare, heavy, radioactive metal used as a fuel in the nuclear industry

Find out more

Books

Air Pollution (Improving Our Environment), Jen Green (Hodder Wayland, 2005)

Is Nuclear Power Safe? (What Do You Think?), Kate Shuster (Heinemann Library, 2007)

Polluted Air (Protect Our Planet), Angela Royston (Heinemann Library, 2008)

Pollution (Earth in Danger), Helen Orme (Ticktock, 2008)

Pollution (Your Environment), Cindy Leaney (Franklin Watts, 2007)

Pollution and Conservation (Discovery Geography) Rebecca Hunter, (Raintree Publishers, 2004)

Websites

This fun website includes lots of information to help children help the environment:
www.kidsforsavingearth.org

Play games and take part in activities and competitions at the award-winning EcoKids website:
www.ecokids.ca

This informative website includes a series of information sheets to help children find out more about air pollution:
www.clean-air-kids.org.uk

Join Tiki the Penguin and find out all about pollution and what you can do to stop it:
http://tiki.oneworld.net/pollution/pollution_home.html

Index